Inspiring | Educating | Creating | Entertaining

Brimming with creative inspiration, how-to projects, and useful information to enrich your everyday life, Quarto Knows is a favourite destination for those pursuing their interests and passions. Visit our site and dig deeper with our books into your area of interest: Quarto Creates, Quarto Cooks, Quarto Homes, Quarto Lives, Quarto Drives, Quarto Explores, Quarto Gifts, or Quarto Kids.

First Published in 2019 by Frances Lincoln Children's Books,
an imprint of The Quarto Group.
400 First Avenue North, Suite 400, Minneapolis, MN 55401, USA.
T (612) 344-8100 F (612) 344-8692 **www.QuartoKnows.com**

A catalogue record for this book is available from the British Library.

ISBN 978-1-78603-337-6

The illustrations were created with thread and needle

Designed by Karissa Santos
Production by Nicolas Zeifman
consultation by AnnMarie Anderson
with thanks to Terry Kluytmans for the extended version of Hickory, Dickory, Dock.

Manufactured in Shenzhen, China HH112018

9 8 7 6 5 4 3 2 1

# Read to your baby every day

Frances Lincoln
Children's Books

# CONTENTS

# Hey,
# Diddle Diddle

Hey diddle, diddle,
The cat and the fiddle,
The cow jumped over the moon,
The little dog laughed,
To see such sport,
And the dish ran away
with the spoon.

# Baa, Baa, Black Sheep

"Baa, baa, black sheep,
Have you any wool?"
"Yes sir, yes sir,
Three bags full.
One for my master,
One for my d dame,
And one for the little boy
Who lives down the lane."

"Baa, baa, white sheep,
Have you any wool?
Yes sir, yes sir,
Three needles full.
One to mend a sweater,
One to mend a frock,
And one for the little girl
With holes in her sock."

# This Little Piggy

This little piggy went to market.
This little piggy stayed at home.
This little piggy had roast beef.
This little piggy had none.
And this little piggy went...
"Wee, wee, wee," all the way home!

# Hush, Little Baby

Hush, little baby, don't say a word.

Papa's gonna buy you a mockingbird.

And if that mockingbird won't sing.

Papa's gonna buy you a diamond ring.

And if that diamond ring turns brass.

Papa's gonna buy you a looking glass.

And if that looking glass gets brote.

Papa's gonna buy you a billy goat.

And if that billy goat won't pull.

Papa's gonna buy you a cart and bull.

And if that cart and bull turn over.

Papa's gonna buy you a dog named Rover.

And if that dog named Rover won't bark.

Papa's gonna buy you a horse and cart.

And if that horse and cart fall down,

You'll still be the sweetest little baby in town.

# Hickory, Dickory, Dock

Hickory, dickory, dock!
The mouse ran up the clock.
The clock struck one.
The mouse ran down.
Hickory, dickory, dock.

Hickory, dickory, dock!
The mouse ran up the clock.
The clock struck three.
And he did flee:
Hickory, dickory, dock.

Hickory, dickory, dock!
The mouse ran up the clock.
The clock struck ten.
The mouse came again:
Hickory, dickory, dock.

# Twinkle, Twinkle, Little Star

Twinkle, twinkle, little star,
How I wonder what you are.
Up above the world so high,
Like a diamond in the sky.
Twinkle, twinkle, little star,
How I wonder what you are!

When the blazing sun is gone,
When he nothing shines upon,
Then you show your little light,
Twinkle, twinkle, through the night.
Twinkle, twinkle, little star,
How I wonder what you are!

# Little Bo-Peep

Little Bo-Peep has lost her sheep.
And doesn't know where to find them.
Leave them alone, and they'll come home.
Wagging their tails behind them.

Little Bo-Peep fell fast asleep.
And dreamt she heard them bleating;
But when she awoke, she found it a joke,
For still they all were fleeting.

Then up she took her little crook,
Determined for to find them,
She found them indeed, but it made her heart bleed,
For they'd left their tails behind them!

It happened one day, as Bo-Peep did stray
Into a meadow nearby,
There she espied their tails side by side,
All hung on a tree to dry.

She heaved a sigh and wiped her eye,
And over the hillocks went rambling,
And tried what she could, as a shepherdess should,
To tack each again to its lambkin.

# Pussy-cat, Pussy-cat

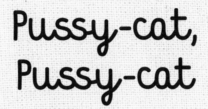

"Pussy-cat, pussy-cat,
Where have you been?"

"I've been up to London
To visit the Queen."

"Pussy-cat, pussy-cat,
What did you there?"

"I frightened a little mouse
Under her chair."

# Row, Row, Row Your Boat

Row, row, row your boat.
Gently down the stream.
Merrily, merrily, merrily, merrily,
Life is but a dream.

Row, row, row your boat.
Gently up the creek.
If you see a little mouse,
Don't forget to squeak!

Row, row, row your boat,
Gently down the stream.
If you see a crocodile,
Don't forget to scream!

Row, row, row your boat,
Gently to the shore.
If you see a lion,
Don't forget to roar!

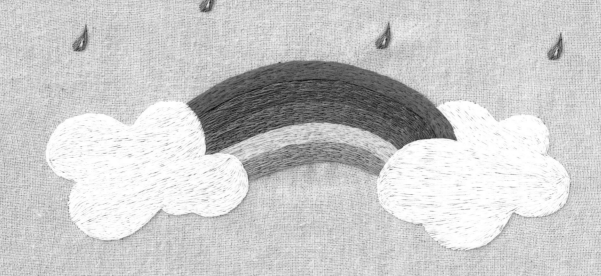

# The Itsy Bitsy Spider

The itsy bitsy spider
Climbed up the water spout.
Down came the rain
And washed the spider out.
Out came the sun
And dried up all the rain.
And the itsy bitsy spider
Climbed up the spout again.

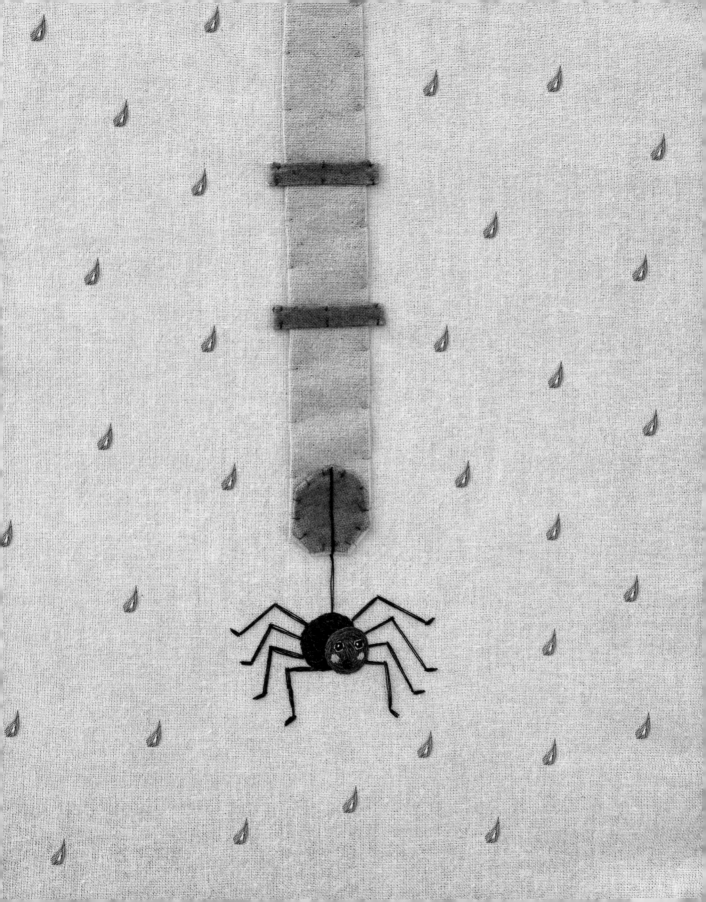

# London Bridge

London Bridge
is falling down.
Falling down, falling down.
London Bridge
is falling down.
My fair lady.

# Mary Had a Little Lamb

Mary had a little lamb.
It's fleece was white as snow;
And everywhere that Mary went
The lamb was sure to go.
He followed her to school one day
Which was against the rule;
It made the children laugh and play.
To see a lamb at school.
And so the teacher turned him out,
But still he lingered near;
And waited patiently about
Till Mary did appear.
"What makes the lamb love Mary so?"
The eager children cry;
"Why, Mary loves the lamb, you know".
The teacher did reply.

# One, Two, Buckle My Shoe

One, two,
Buckle my shoe;
Three, four,
Knock at the door;
Five, six,
Pick up sticks;
Seven, eight,
Lay them straight;
Nine, ten,
A big fat hen;

Eleven, twelve,
Dig and delve;
Thirteen, fourteen,
Maids a-courting;
Fifteen, sixteen,
Maids in the kitchen;
Seventeen, eighteen,
Maids in waiting;
Nineteen, twenty,
My plate is empty!

# Humpty Dumpty

Humpty Dumpty sat on a wall.
Humpty Dumpty had a great fall.
All the king's horses and all the king's men
Couldn't put Humpty together again!

# Rub-a-dub-dub

Rub-a-dub-dub.

Three men in a tub.

And who do you think they be?

The butcher, the baker.

The candlestick maker.

And all of them out to sea.

# Pat-a-Cake

Pat-a-cake, pat-a-cake, baker's man.
Bake me a cake as fast as you can.
Pat it, and prick it, and mark it with "B".
Put it in the oven for baby and me.

Pat-a-cake, pat-a-cake, baker's man,
Bake me a cake as fast as you can.
Make it with chocolate, make it with cream,
Make it the prettiest you ever have seen.

Pat-a-cake, pat-a-cake, baker's man.

Bake me a cake as fast as you can.

Mix it, and stir it, and bake it just right,

Good from the first 'til the very last bite.


Pat-a-cake, pat-a-cake, baker's man.

Bake me a cake as fast as you can.

Write his name with lots of care,

And ice pretty flowers here and there.

# I Saw a Ship A-Sailing

I saw a ship a-sailing.
A-sailing on the sea.
And it was full of pretty things
For baby and for me.
There were sweetmeats in the cabin.
And apples in the hold.
The sails were made of silk.
And the masts were made of gold.
The four-and-twenty sailors
That stood between the decks.
Were four-and-twenty white mice.
With chains about their necks.

The captain was a duck.
With a packet on his back.
And when the ship began to move.
The captain cried. "Alas. alack!"
I saw a ship a-sailing.
A-sailing on the sea.
And it was full of pretty things
For baby and for me.

# Old MacDonald

Old MacDonald had a farm. E-I-E-I-O.
And on his farm he had a cow. E-I-E-I-O.
With a moo-moo here, and a moo-moo there.
Here a moo,
There a moo,
Everywhere moo-moo.
Old MacDonald had a farm. E-I-E-I-O.


Old MacDonald had a farm. E-I-E-I-O.
And on his farm he had a pig, E-I-E-I-O.
With an oink-oink here, and an oink-oink there.
Here an oink,
There an oink,
Everywhere oink-oink.
Old MacDonald had a farm. E-I-E-I-O.

Old MacDonald had a farm, E-I-E-I-O.
And on his farm he had a duck, E-I-E-I-O.
With a quack-quack here, and a quack-quack there,
Here a quack,
There a quack,
Everywhere quack-quack.
Old MacDonald had a farm, E-I-E-I-O.

Old MacDonald had a farm, E-I-E-I-O.
And on his farm he had a horse, E-I-E-I-O.
With a neigh-neigh here, and a neigh-neigh there,
Here a neigh,
There a neigh,
Everywhere neigh-neigh.
Old MacDonald had a farm, E-I-E-I-O.

# Hush-a-Bye Baby

Hush-a-bye baby on the tree top.
When the wind blows the cradle will rock;
When the bough breaks the cradle will fall.
Down will come baby. bough. cradle and all.

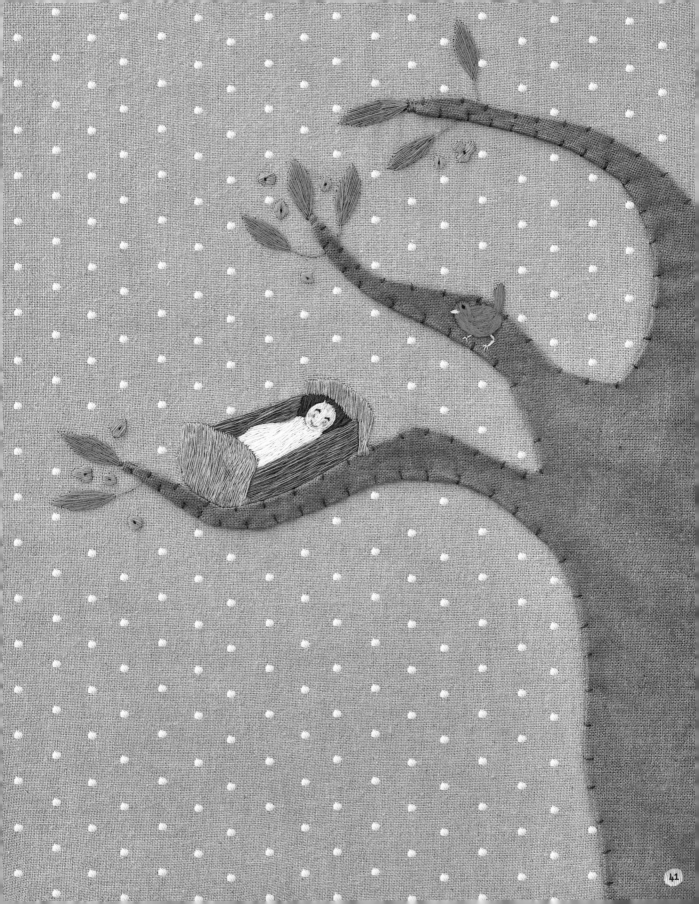

# The Wheels on the Bus

The wheels on the bus go round and round,
Round and round, round and round.
The wheels on the bus go round and round,
All day long.

The wipers on the bus go swish, swish, swish,
Swish, swish, swish, swish, swish, swish.
The wipers on the bus go swish, swish, swish,
All day long.

The horn on the bus goes beep, beep, beep,
Beep, beep, beep, beep, beep, beep.
The horn on the bus go beep, beep, beep,
All day long.

The children on the bus go chatter, chatter, chatter,
Chatter, chatter, chatter, chatter, chatter, chatter.
The children on the bus go chatter, chatter, chatter,
All day long.

The people on the bus go up and down,
Up and down, up and down.
The people on the bus go up and down.
All day long.

The money on the bus goes, clink, clink, clink,
Clink, clink, clink, clink, clink, clink.
The money on the bus goes, clink, clink, clink,
All day long.

The driver on the bus says "Move on back,
move on back, move on back"
The Driver on the bus says "Move on back",
All day long.

# I'm a Little Teapot

I am a little teapot.

Short and stout.

Here is my handle.

Here is my spout.


When the water's boiling.

Hear me shout!

Pick me up

And pour me out.


I am a little teapot.

Short and stout.

Here is my handle.

Here is my spout.


When the water's boiling.

Hear me shout!

Pick me up

And pour me out.

# This Old Man

This old man, he played one,
He played knick-knack on my thumb,
With a knick-knack paddy wack
Give a dog a bone,
This old man came rolling home.

This old man, he played two,
He played knick-knack on my shoe,
With a knick-knack paddy wack
Give a dog a bone,
This old man came rolling home.

This old man, he played three,
He played knick-knack on my knee,
With a knick-knack paddy wack
Give a dog a bone,
This old man came rolling home.

This old man, he played four,
He played knick-knack on my door.
With a knick-knack paddy wack
Give a dog a bone,
This old man came rolling home.

This old man, he played five,
Don't play knick-knack on that hive.
With a knick-knack paddy wack
Give a dog a bone,
This old man came rolling home.

This old man, he played six,
He played knick-knack on my sticks.
With a knick-knack paddy wack
Give a dog a bone,
This old man came rolling home.

This old man, he played seven,
He played knick-knack up in heaven.
With a knick-knack paddy wack
Give a dog a bone,
This old man came rolling home.

This old man, he played eight,
He played knick-knack on my gate,
With a knick-knack paddy wack
Give a dog a bone,
This old man came rolling home.

This old man, he played nine,
He played knick-knack on my vine,
With a knick-knack paddy wack
Give a dog a bone,
This old man came rolling home.

This old man, he played ten,
He played knick-knack all over again,
With a knick-knack paddy wack
Give a dog a bone,
This old man came rolling home.

# Jack and Jill

Jack and Jill went up the hill
To fetch a pail of water.
Jack fell down and broke his crown,
And Jill came tumbling after.
Up Jack got, and home did trot,
As fast as he could caper.
He went to bed to mend his head,
With vinegar and brown paper.

# The Muffin Man

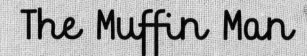

Oh, do you know the muffin man,
The muffin man, the muffin man,
Oh, do you know the muffin man,
Who lives on Drury Lane?

Oh, yes, I know the muffin man,
The muffin man, the muffin man,
Oh, yes, I know the muffin man,
Who lives on Drury Lane.

# Little Miss Muffet

Little Miss Muffet sat on a tuffet,
Eating her curds and whey.
Along came a spider
Who sat down beside her
And frightened Miss Muffet away.

# The Owl and
# the Pussy-cat

The Owl and the Pussy-cat went to sea
In a beautiful pea-green boat.
They took some honey, and plenty of money,
Wrapped up in a five-pound note.
The Owl looked up to the stars above,
And sang to a small guitar,
"O lovely Pussy! O Pussy, my love,
What a beautiful Pussy you are,
You are!
What a beautiful Pussy you are!"

# Here We Go Round the Mulberry Bush

Here we go round the mulberry bush.
The mulberry bush.
The mulberry bush.
Here we go round the mulberry bush
On a cold and frosty morning.

This is the way we wash our face.
Wash our face.
Wash our face.
This is the way we wash our face
On a cold and frosty morning.

This is the way we comb our hair.
Comb our hair.
Comb our hair.
This is the way we comb our hair
On a cold and frosty morning.

This is the way we brush our teeth.
Brush our teeth.
Brush our teeth.
This is the way we brush our teeth
On a cold and frosty morning.

This is the way we put on our clothes.
Put on our clothes.
Put on our clothes.
This is the way we put on our clothes
On a cold and frosty morning.

Here we go round the mulberry bush.
The mulberry bush.
The mulberry bush.
Here we go round the mulberry bush
On a cold and frosty morning.

# Old Mother Hubbard

Old Mother Hubbard
Went to the cupboard.
To give her poor dog a bone;
But when she got there
The cupboard was bare.
And so the poor dog had none.

She went to the baker's
To buy him some bread;
When she came back
The dog was dead!

She went to the undertaker's
To buy him a coffin;
When she came back
The dog was laughing.

She took a clean dish
to get him some tripe;

When she came back
He was smoking his pipe.

She went to the alehouse
To get him some beer;
When she came back
The dog sat in a chair.

She went to the tavern
For white wine and red;
When she came back
The dog stood on his head.

She went to the grocer's
To buy him some fruit;
When she came back
He was playing the flute.

She went to the tailor's
To buy him a coat;
When she came back
He was riding a goat.

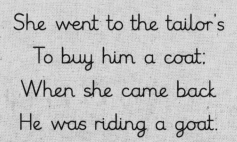

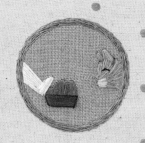

She went to the hatter's
To buy him a hat;
When she came back
He was feeding her cat.

She went to the barber's
To buy him a wig;
When she came back
He was dancing a jig.

She went to the cobbler's
To buy him some shoes;
When she came back
He was reading the news.

She went to the seamstress
To buy him some linen;
When she came back
The dog was spinning.

She went to the hosier's
To buy him some hose;
When she came back
He was dressed in his clothes.

The Dame made a curtsy,
The dog made a bow;
The Dame said, "Your servant",
The dog said, "Bow-wow".

This wonderful dog
Was Dame Hubbard's delight.
He could read, he could dance,
He could sing, he could write.
She gave him rich dainties
Whenever he fed,
And erected this monument
When he was dead.

# Pop! Goes the Weasel

Half a pound of tuppenny rice.
Half a pound of treacle.
That's the way the money goes.
Pop! goes the weasel.

# Are You Sleeping?

Are you sleeping, are you sleeping?
Brother John, Brother John?
Morning bells are ringing, Morning bells are ringing.
Ding Dang Dong, Ding Dang Dong.


[French]
Frère Jacques, Frère Jacques,
Dormez vous? Dormez vous?
Sonnez les matines, Sonnez les matines
Ding Dang Dong, Ding Dang Dong.